D.I.Y. MAN

 Robson Books

First published in Great Britain in 1989 by Robson Books Ltd,
Bolsover House, 5–6 Clipstone Street, London W1P 7EB

Copyright © 1989 Larry

British Library Cataloguing in Publication Data

Larry
  Larry's DIY man.
  1. English humorous cartoons
  I. Title
  741.5'942

ISBN 0 86051 585 0

Printed and bound in Great Britain by
Biddles Ltd, Guildford and King's Lynn

This book is dedicated to the memory of the original DIY man, Barry Bucknall, who graced our black and white TV screens in the Fifties showing us how to flush panel our moulded doors, block in our balustraded staircases and in all manner of means modernize our homes. Anything that might collect dust was covered up — with formica. Fashions change and the formica is coming off sometimes, if you're lucky, revealing a Victorian cast iron fireplace (£400 each in Hampstead shops).

Thanks to Mr Bucknall — undoing his handiwork is more fun for the modern DIY man than anything else on offer.

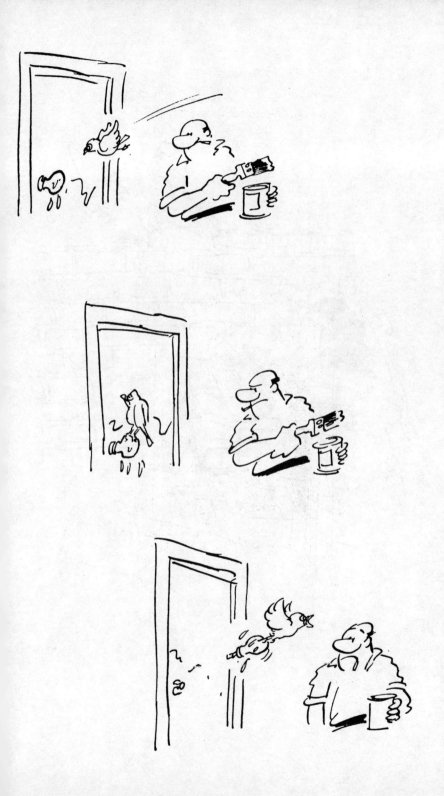

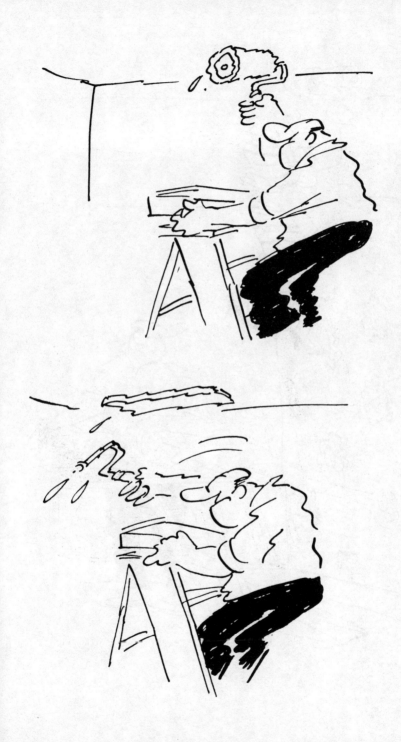

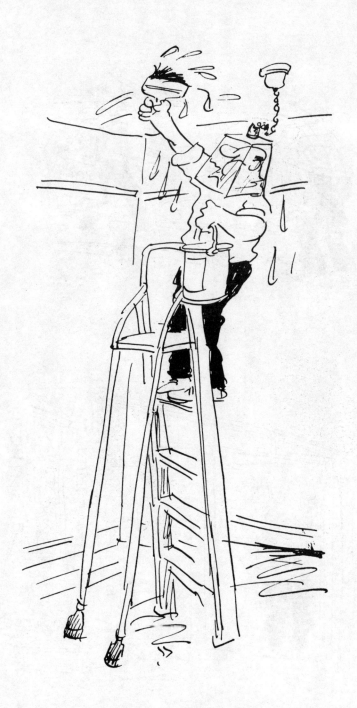